Through Geography

KEY STAGE 1: Y1–2

FRANCES MACKAY

HOPSCOTCH
EDUCATIONAL PUBLISHING

Contents

Published by Hopscotch Educational Publishing Ltd,
29 Waterloo Place, Leamington Spa CV32 5LA
(Tel: 01926 744227)

© 2001 Hopscotch Educational Publishing

Written by Frances Mackay
Series design by Blade Communications
Illustrated by Claire Boyce
Cover illustrated by Susan Hutchinson
Printed by Clintplan, Southam

Frances Mackay hereby asserts her moral right to be identified as
the author of this work in accordance with the Copyright, Designs
and Patents Act, 1988.

ISBN 1-902239-75-X

Introduction

ABOUT THE SERIES

Developing Literacy Skills Through Geography is a series of books aimed at developing key literacy skills using a range of written genres and diagrams based on a geographical theme, from Key Stage 1 through to Key Stage 2.

The series offers a structured approach which provides detailed lesson plans to teach specific literacy and geographical skills. A unique feature of the series is the provision of differentiated photocopiable activities aimed at considerably reducing teacher preparation time. Suggestions for follow-up activities for both literacy and geography ensure maximum use of this resource.

ABOUT THIS BOOK

This book is for teachers of children at Key Stage 1, Years 1–2. It aims to:
+ develop children's literacy and geography skills through exposure to and experience of a wide range of stimulating texts with supporting differentiated activities which are both diversified and challenging;
+ support teachers by providing practical teaching methods based on whole-class, group, paired and individual teaching;
+ encourage enjoyment and curiosity as well as develop skills of interpretation and response.

CHAPTER CONTENT

 Literacy objectives

This outlines the aims for the literacy activities suggested in the lesson plan.

 Geography objectives

This outlines the geography learning objectives that relate to the lesson plan.

 Resources

This lists the different resources that the teacher needs to teach the lesson.

 Starting point: Whole class

This provides ideas for introducing the activity and may include key questions to ask the children.

 Using the photocopiable text/ diagram

This explains how to use the whole-class text/diagram with the children as a shared reading activity and introduction to the group work. It may also be used by groups during the group work.

 Group activities

This explains how to use each sheet as well as providing guidance on the type of child who will benefit most from each sheet.

 Plenary session

This suggests ideas for whole-class sessions to discuss the learning outcomes and follow-up work.

 Follow-up ideas for literacy

This contains suggestions for further literacy activities related to the lesson plan which can be carried out at another time.

 Follow-up ideas for geography

This contains suggestions for further geography activities related to the lesson plan which can be carried out at another time.

Where I live

Literacy objectives

✦ To recognise capital letters. (Y1: T1, S5)
✦ To know that a line of writing is not necessarily the same as a sentence. (Y1: T1, S7)
✦ To read and use captions. (Y1: T1, T12)
✦ To write captions. (Y1: T1, T14)

Geography objectives

(Unit 1)
✦ To know that all children have a personal address.
✦ To know own address.
✦ To understand the significance of each line of address.
✦ To use geographical vocabulary.

Resources

✦ A collection of old envelopes with names and addresses on them.

Starting point: Whole class

✦ Ideally, before the lesson, photocopy page 6 (enough for each child to have a copy) and put the letters into envelopes with the children's full names and addresses on them. This means that each child will receive a copy of the letter as well as having a copy of their own address to use as a reference point during the lesson.
✦ Ask the children if they have ever received a letter. Can they remember how it was addressed? Explain that all of them have their own personal address which is different from other people's. Why would this be important? Share the collection of old envelopes, showing a variety of different names and addresses. Write one of the addresses (or the school's address) on the board. What do the children notice about how it is set out?
✦ Tell them that addresses are set out in a particular way and that each part of the address is on a separate line. Go through each line of the address explaining its significance. Label each part of the address with suitable captions, for example 'name', 'house number', 'street', 'town', 'county', 'country' and 'postcode'. Discuss the meaning of each term and why it is an important part of the address.
✦ Ask the children to point out the capital letters in the address. Where are they used? Why are they used there? When else do we use capitals?

Using the photocopiable text

✦ Tell the children that today they are all going to receive a letter! Hand out the envelopes with page 6 inside. Tell them to look carefully at their name and address on the envelope. Is it correct? How many of them know their complete address? Why might it be important to know their own address?
✦ Ask them to open the envelopes and read out the letter to them as they follow it. Discuss what the letter is about. Why do they think it was written? You could ask questions about the letter to explore its content as well as the geographical vocabulary. For example, 'In what country does Jo live?', 'What country did the people living next door to Jo come from?', 'What is the name of the street where Jo lives?' and 'Did Jo use to live in a city or a village?'
✦ What do the children notice about how the letter is set out? Look at the address. Revise the features of each line using the example written on the board.
✦ Ask the children to find the capital letters in the address. Where else are there capital letters in the letter? Remind them about how sentences begin with a capital letter and end with a full stop. Find the sentences. Explain how the letter is set out in lines (the address is also in lines) but that a line of writing is not necessarily the same as a sentence. (You could enlarge a copy of the letter to use here. Circle one paragraph and ask the children 'How many lines?' and 'How many sentences?' Count them together.)
✦ Use an enlarged version of the letter (or write the address on the board) and ask the children to label the address with the following captions: 'house number', 'street', 'town', 'county', 'country' and 'postcode'.
✦ Tell the children that they will now be doing an activity using addresses.

Group activities

Using the differentiated activity sheets

Activity sheet 1: This sheet is aimed at children who can recognise capital letters and can match simple captions. They are also required to write their own name and address. They could use the envelope (with their own name and address on it) given out in the whole-class session as a model.

Where I live

Activity sheet 2: This sheet is aimed at children who can write capital letters and captions. They are also required to write their own name and address.

Activity sheet 3: This sheet is for more able children. They are required to add the correct capital letters in an address and to label each line of an address. They are also required to write their own name and address.

 Plenary session

Share the responses to the activity sheets. Did the children remember to use capital letters correctly? Did they have any problems with selecting the captions? How many lines are there in their own addresses? Compare. Ask the children to remind you why it is important for them to know their own address.

 Follow-up ideas for literacy

- ✦ Use the letter as a model for the children to write their own letters to each other. You could provide envelopes and a postbox.
- ✦ Ask the children to write some sentences about where they live. Use the activity to reinforce knowledge about capital letters and full stops. Make a class book with drawings of the children's houses together with their sentences.
- ✦ Share poems on a theme of homes/ where we live. Use the poems to reinforce the concept that a line of writing is not necessarily a sentence.

- ✦ Use the letter to begin a discussion about moving house or visiting other people's homes. Ask the children to write about their personal experiences.
- ✦ Ask the children to draw a picture of their house or street and write captions to label it. For example: roof, garden, road, gate, lamp, window, door.
- ✦ Ask the children to write a story about Jo's moving day. What happened at the beginning of the journey? Why did it take two days? What happened when they arrived? What happened next?

 Follow-up ideas for geography

- ✦ Put on display a map of the local area. Ask the children to write labels with their own name and address. Put the labels around the map. Attach string to each label to show the location of the address on the map.
- ✦ Go on a walk around the local area to locate some of the children's addresses. Take photographs. Make a display of the photos and ask the children to write sentences about them and their relationship to the school. For example, 'This is Ahmed's house. He lives in Pride's Lane. He has a short walk to school.'

- ✦ Carry out a survey of how the children come to school: on foot, by car, bus, bicycle and so on. Make a simple pictogram of the results. Ask questions about the pictogram, such as 'How many children walk to school?', 'What is the most common way that children in our class come to school?' and 'Do more children walk to school than come by bus?' Discuss the findings. For example, do they think it is better to walk to school or come by car? Why? Are there any problems if lots of people come to school by car? Which is the safest way to come to school? Why?

12 High Street
New Town
Wiltshire
England
NT11 2PP

22nd January

My dear friend,

Well, here I am at last! It took us two days to get here but now we are at our new house. I wish you could see it! It is really nice.

On Monday we went for a long walk. It is only a small town, not like the big city where you live but it is bigger than our old village. I like it here.

The people in the house next door are very nice. They come from another country called Denmark. They said they have lived in our street for 10 years and they are very happy here.

My new school is not very far away. I will be able to walk there. Mum is going to walk there and back with me because we have to cross a very busy road. The school is much bigger than my old school. I hope I make some new friends.

Please write soon.

Love Jo

◆ Addresses ◆

◆ Look at the address below. Draw a line from each label to the correct part of the address. One has been done for you.

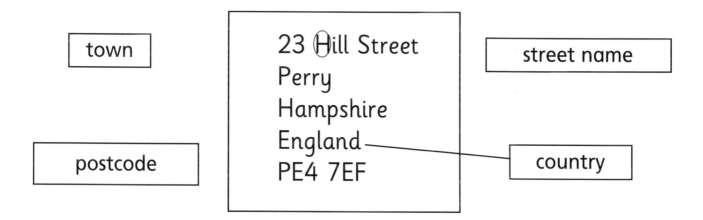

town

street name

23 (H)ill Street
Perry
Hampshire
England
PE4 7EF

postcode

country

◆ Circle all the capital letters. One has been done for you.

◆ Now write your own name and address on the envelope below. Remember to use capital letters where you need to.

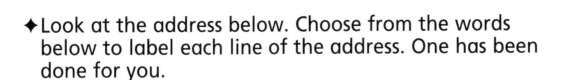

◆ Addresses ◆

◆ Look at the address below. Choose from the words below to label each line of the address. One has been done for you.

```
23 Hill Street
Perry
Hampshire
England
PE4 7EF
```

house number and street name
_____

_____

_____

_____

| postcode | | country | | town |

| house number and street name | | county |

◆ The street name below does not have capital letters in it. Rewrite it, putting in the capitals.

14 walker street

_____

◆ On the back of this sheet, write your name and full address as they would be written on an envelope.

◆ Addresses ◆

◆Look at the address below. All the capital letters
  are missing. Rewrite the address with the capital letters.

23 hill street
perry
hampshire
england
pe4 7ef

_____

_____

_____

_____

_____

◆Label each line of the address below.
  The first one has been done for you.

5 Pine Street
Wellow
Somerset
England
SO4 7ER

house number and street name

_____

_____

_____

_____

◆On the back of this sheet, write your name and full address
  as they would be written on an envelope.

Chapter 2

Getting to school

 Literacy objectives

♦ To read and follow simple instructions. (Y1: T1, T3)
♦ To write simple instructions and labels. (Y1: T1, T16)

 Geography objectives

(Unit 1)
♦ To describe a route.
♦ To understand sense of place in relation to home and school.
♦ To draw a map showing their route to school.
♦ To use geographical vocabulary.

 Resources

♦ Sets of directions relating to the classroom.

 Starting point: Whole class

♦ Have prepared some simple sets of directions relating to the classroom (or hall/playground) with objects, such as a bookcase, set out. One set of directions might read, for example, 'Face the blackboard, walk to the reading corner, turn right, walk to the teacher's desk, stop.' Write the instructions on separate, large sheets of paper.
♦ Tell the children that today they are going to be thinking about how they can get from one place to another. Pin up the first set of directions. Read them out. Ask someone to tell you what the instructions are telling us to do. Choose a child to stand at the place where the directions begin. Read out the directions again together, more slowly this time, so that the child can follow the route. Revise knowledge of left and right if necessary.
♦ Repeat the process with the other sets of directions, using different children to follow the route. Ask the children to tell you why they think it might be important for us to use sets of instructions like these. (Visitors to the school may want to know how to get to the office, for example.) When else might we use directions? Discuss ideas such as going to someone's house for a party or finding a particular shop.
♦ Look at the words used in the directions. How important is it to use the terms 'left' and 'right'? How does this help us? How important is it to mention particular objects/ features, such as the reading corner, for example? Talk about how it is important to pick out certain things along the route as 'markers'.

♦ Finally, ask a child to walk a route of their own choice in the classroom. The others should watch very carefully. Together, agree how to write the directions for this route.

 Using the photocopiable text

♦ Tell the children that they are now going to look at a set of instructions that explain how to get to a school. Share an enlarged version of page 12 or provide each pair with a copy.
♦ Explain that the school is having a fete and they have sent out invitations with a map and set of directions.
♦ Read the invitation and then discuss the map and directions. Explain that when we are looking at a map we have to imagine being there, so if we were walking along High Street from the direction of Smithton we would turn left to go into Hill Street, not right. (Many children may find this difficult to understand – but do not worry about this at this stage – the practice in describing a route is what is important here.)
♦ Discuss other possible routes on the map, for example how to get from house number 3 to the garage. Agree together as a class how to write the directions.
♦ Next, ask the children to think about their own route to school. How far away do they live? How might they give the directions? Ask them to sit in pairs and try and describe their journey to school. What features do they pass? What roads do they cross? (You could follow up this activity by asking the children to draw and label a map of their route to school.)

 Group activities

Using the differentiated activity sheets

Activity sheet 1: This sheet is aimed at children who can follow a simple route on a map and complete a set of directions using the support of a word box.

Activity sheet 2: This sheet is similar to Activity sheet 1 but here the children are required to recognise left or right turns. They have less support with completing the directions. They are also required to label the crossings on the map.

Getting to school

Activity sheet 3: This sheet is for more able children. They are required to label the map using the class text as a model and then write their own directions for the marked route.

 Plenary session

Share the responses to the activity sheets. Do the children agree on the words used to complete the set of directions? Discuss the importance of accuracy in giving or writing instructions on how to get to a place.

 Follow-up ideas for literacy

+ Use the invitation as a model for the children to write their own invitations. You could arrange a special event to which other classes are invited.
+ Look at other sets of instructions such as recipes, board-games and so on. Discuss the importance of correct sequencing. Provide the children with pictures and/or sentences from a set of instructions and ask them to sequence them.
+ Have fun making up gruesome recipes.

+ Ask the children to imagine what the fete at Rosetta Primary School might be like. Agree a class list of things that might be there for people to do, look at and buy. The children could use the word list to draw some pictures and write some sentences about what the fete might be like.
+ Ask the children to draw a map of their own school and the nearest streets. They could write captions to label it.

 Follow-up ideas for geography

+ Go on a walk around the streets nearest the school. What 'landmarks' are there on the way that the children could use to give people directions? What are the names of the streets?
+ Agree a set of directions for getting to particular places in the school (from the classroom), such as the office, the hall or the playground. Then use the agreed directions to walk the route. How good are the directions? Has anything important been left out? Are the left and right directions correct?

+ Show the children some photographs taken at various places in and around the school. Can they recognise them? Can they explain how to get to these places from where they are? This could be extended to pictures of buildings and features near the school.
+ Discuss safety issues relating to the children's journeys to school. Where are the safest places to cross roads? Why is it important to use crossings? What changes could be made to the local area to make it safer for people to walk to school?

Invitation

You are invited to
our school
FÊTE
on
Saturday 7th July 2001
at 2 pm

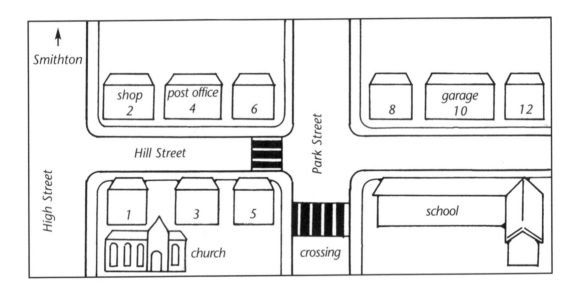

Directions

1. From Smithton, turn left into Hill Street at the shop.
2. Go past the post office.
3. Cross at the crossing near number 6 Hill Street.
4. Cross at the crossing in Park Street.

◆ Writing directions ◆

◆ Look at the map below. It is a map showing how to get
from the church to Rosetta Primary School.

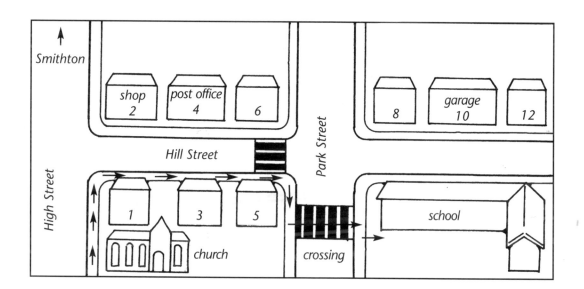

◆ Now complete the directions below using the words in the box.

crossing	Street	Park
houses	Hill	

1. From the church walk up High Street.

2. Turn right into Hill _____

3. Go past the _____ at numbers 1, 3
   and 5 _____ Street.

4. Turn right into _____ Street.

5. Cross at the _____ in Park Street.

✦ Writing directions ✦

✦Look at the map below. It is a map showing how to get from the church to Rosetta Primary School.

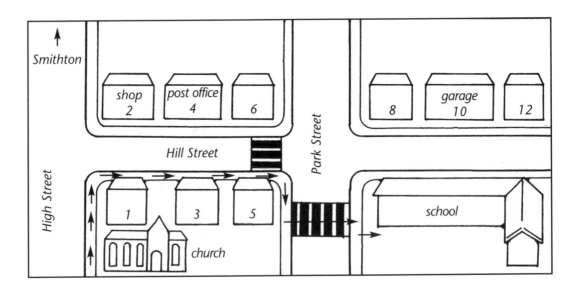

✦Now complete the directions below using the words in the box.

crossing	right	Street	Park
church	houses	Hill	High

1. From the _____ walk up _____ Street.

2. Turn _____ into Hill _____

3. Go past the _____ at numbers 1, 3 and 5

    _____ Street.

4. Turn _____ into _____ Street.

5. Cross at the _____ in _____ Street.

✦Label the two crossings on the map.

✦ Writing directions ✦

✦ Label the following places on the map below. Use the class text to help you.

High Street shop	Hill Street post office	Park Street school	crossing garage

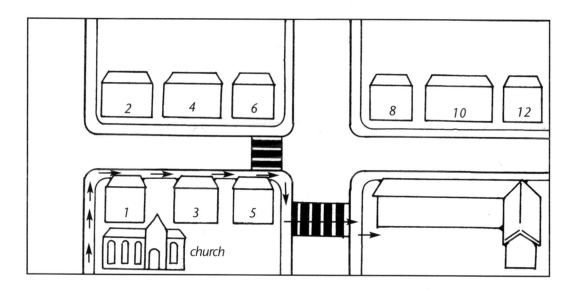

✦ Look carefully at the arrows showing the route from the church to the school. Write the directions for this route. The first part has been done for you.

1. From the church walk up High Street.

_____

_____

_____

_____

_____

©Hopscotch Educational Publishing

Chapter 3

People at work

Literacy objectives

- To identify and discuss characters; to discuss how they are described in the text. (Y1: T2, T8)
- To write a simple character profile. (Y1: T2, T15)

Geography objectives

(Unit 1)

- To recognise that different places in an area support different kinds of work.

Resources

- Pictures of people doing different jobs, for example a nurse, a baker and a shopkeeper.
- Pictures of different places of work, for example a garage, a hospital, a factory, an office block and a post office.

Starting point: Whole class

- Tell the children that they are going to share a story about a man called Mr Appleby. Explain that the story tells us what happened to him one day at work. Tell them that he works in a village. Can they predict where he might work? Make a list on the board, such as post office, shop, garage, newsagent, bank, doctor's surgery, farm, school, church and police station.

Using the photocopiable text

- Share an enlarged version of page 18 or provide each pair with a copy.
- Discuss what happens in the story. Why is Mr Appleby sad when he goes home that day?
- Discuss Mr Appleby's character. Begin by looking at the pictures. What does he look like? How old do the children think he is? What does he wear at work? Why would he need to wear this?
- Talk about Mr Appleby's behaviour. Why was he in a bad mood when he left home in the morning? Why was he worried as he walked to work? What kinds of things was he always doing? What did other people tend to think of him? What qualities did he have that made people like him? Why do they think Mr Devon was not

so happy with him? What do they think Mr Appleby will do now that he has lost his job?

- Remind the children that Mr Appleby worked in a village. Look at the list of places of work written on the board at the beginning of the lesson. In which of these places do they think he might be able to get a job? Why?
- Ask the children to think about the jobs that people do in their local area. How do they compare with those listed on the board? Show them the collection of pictures to help their ideas. Compare the jobs that might be available in a village, a town and a large city. What might affect the jobs people can do? For example, if coal is found in a particular area then mining might take place there; farmers wouldn't be able to work in a city because there wouldn't be any farm land there.
- Tell the children that you now want them to think about all the things you discussed about Mr Appleby in order to write about him. Explain that while they are doing this you want them to think carefully about the kind of new job he might be able to find in his village.

People at work

 ## Group activities

Using the differentiated activity sheets

Activity sheet 1: This sheet is aimed at children who can match labels to a picture and can use words from a word box to complete some sentences.

Activity sheet 2: This sheet is aimed at children who can write labels, choosing from a list of words available and can complete sentences using words in a word box.

Activity sheet 3: This sheet is for more able children. They are required to label a picture and write their own sentences. They are also required to list the kinds of jobs that might be available in a village.

 ## Plenary session

Share the responses to the activity sheets. Can the children agree on the kind of job Mr Appleby might be able to get? For example, if he is kind and friendly, might he be good in a shop?

 ## Follow-up ideas for literacy

- Ask the children to complete the story about Mr Appleby. What happens next? Does Mr Devon help him? Does he find a better job?
- Role-play the story, taking note of the narration and dialogue. How do they think Mr Devon might speak? Mr Appleby? Invent Mrs Waverley's character and how she may have reacted.
- Share other stories about people at work, such as the *Happy Families* series by Janet and Allen Ahlberg. Ask the children to write their own story about a person at work.

- Use the text to explore capital letters. Where are they used in the story? When else do we use capitals? Make up names for customers who might visit the garage. Make up possible names for the village in the story.
- Use information books to find out about jobs. Make a class book with pictures, captions and sentences about the kinds of jobs people do in the local area or the kinds of jobs the children want to do when they grow up.

 ## Follow-up ideas for geography

- Go on a walk around the local area looking at the land use and the types of buildings. Take photographs and ask the children to draw what they see. Discuss the kinds of jobs that might exist in the area.
- Visit a person at work or ask someone to come to the school to talk about their job. Discuss with the children the kinds of questions they might ask this person. What kinds of things do they have to do in their job?

- Look at the leisure facilities in the local area. What kinds of things do people do after work? Survey the children's parents/ guardians to find out. Compare this with the kinds of things the children like to do in their spare time. Does the local area cater for both? What things could be improved?
- Ask the children to label a large map of the area with the types of businesses and leisure facilities discovered through their walk and survey.

Mr Appleby's job

Tom Appleby left home in a very bad mood. His alarm clock failed to go off and now he was late for work.

"What will Mr Devon say when I get there? It's the third time I've been late this week," he thought as he raced along the street.

Finally he arrived at the garage.

"At last!" yelled Mr Devon. "I thought you were never going to come. At least now I can go to the bank."

Mr Devon didn't wait for Tom's reply. He walked quickly out of the office and was gone.

Tom sighed. He had worked at the garage in the village for only three weeks and he had tried hard to do a good job but things always seemed to go wrong. As he pulled on his blue overalls he thought about the time last week when he accidentally spilt oil all over the seats of Mrs Waverley's new car. He hadn't meant to do it. It just happened. Things always seemed to just happen to Tom! People liked him, though, because he was always very kind and friendly. They even seemed to forgive him

when he did things wrong. Mr Devon, however, was not in a forgiving mood. He came back from the bank looking very worried.

"I'm sorry," he said, "but I just can't afford to keep you on any more. I'll ask around to see if there are any other jobs going. There's bound to be something."

But Tom wasn't so sure.

"I wonder what other work I could do," he thought as he walked home sadly.

✦ Mr Appleby ✦

✦Here is a picture of Mr Appleby. Match the labels to the picture to say what he looks like. One has been done for you.

hat

thin hair

glasses

round face

overalls

fat body

✦Use the words in the box to complete the sentences below.

sad	late	worked
good	kind	

1. Mr Appleby _____ at the garage.

2. He was often _____ for work.

3. Mr Appleby always tried to do a _____ job.

4. People liked him because he was _____ and friendly.

5. He felt very _____ when he lost his job.

Name _____

◆ Mr Appleby ◆

◆ Here is a picture of Mr Appleby. Describe what he looks like by choosing words from the box to label the picture.

thin body	round face	fat body	glasses
young	old thin hair	thin face	
wears a hat	beard	wears overalls	

◆ Complete these sentences about Mr Appleby using the words in the box.

Mr Appleby _____ at the _____

garage. He was often _____ for work. He

always _____ to do a _____ job at work

but things didn't always go _____. People

liked Mr Appleby because he was _____

and _____. He lost his job _____

Mr Devon couldn't afford to keep him on. Now he

is very _____ because he has to find a new job.

sad
friendly
village
because
right
good
worked
late
kind
tried

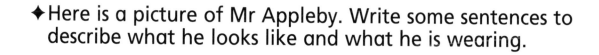

✦ Mr Appleby ✦

✦ Here is a picture of Mr Appleby. Write some sentences to describe what he looks like and what he is wearing.

_____
_____
_____
_____
_____
_____
_____
_____
_____

✦ Write a description of what Mr Appleby was like. What was he like at work? What did people think of him? How did he feel when he lost his job? Use the words in the box to help you.

_____
_____
_____
_____
_____
_____
_____
_____
_____

| sad |
| kind |
| friendly |
| late |
| tried hard |
| made mistakes |
| worried |
| garage |
| village |

✦ On the back of this sheet, list the kinds of jobs you think Mr Appleby's village might have. Then write a sentence saying which new job you think he might get and why.

How places change

 ## Literacy objectives

+ To read a variety of poems on a similar theme. (Y1: T3, T9)
+ To use poems as models for own writing. (Y1: T2, T15)

 ## Geography objectives

(Unit 1)
+ To understand how places change for better or worse over time.

 ## Resources

+ Pictures of places where changes are taking place, such as building sites.
+ If possible, some photographs of changes that have taken place in the local area, for example pictures of a street in the past and now.

 ## Starting point: Whole class

+ Tell the children that they are going to be thinking about how things in their local area change over time. Ask them to tell you about any changes they have noticed taking place near where they live. For example, has someone built an extension to their house? Has someone improved their garden? What about at school – have any changes taken place there? Why do they think these changes were made?
+ Show the children some photographs of a street in the past and the same street now. What changes can they see in the pictures? Why do they think these changes took place?
+ Show them the pictures of things where changes are taking place, for example a building site. What do they think is happening in the pictures? What do they think the place might have been like before? What do they think it might be like after the changes?
+ Remind the children about all the changes they have discussed and draw two columns on the board, one labelled 'good changes' and the other 'bad changes'. Can the children agree to which column the changes they have discussed might belong? Can some changes be both good and bad? Encourage them to try and see both sides of changes that take place. For example, a house built on a field could be a good change for the person owning the land because they can make some

money from this, but it might not be good for the animals and plants that once lived there.
+ Tell the children that they are now going to read some poems about places that have changed. Ask them to think about whether the changes described have been good ones or bad ones.

 ## Using the photocopiable text

+ Share an enlarged version of page 24 or provide each pair with a copy.
+ Share the poems. Discuss what is happening in each one. Talk about the changes that have occurred in these places. Were the changes good, bad or both?
+ Talk about the poems in general. Which poem do the children like best? Why? Why do they think the poets have written them? Are they trying to give us a message? How are the poems similar? How are they different?
+ Discuss the repeating pattern in 'Walking round the town'. Model how to write new verses for the poem by asking the children to invent other changes that might have taken place.
+ Note: 'Where we used to play' is an action poem. The children could make up actions to go with each verse and then perform it. This poem could also be changed by altering some of the words, for example:

Here are the <u>bushes</u>	Here comes the <u>mole</u>
Standing big and tall.	<u>Small</u>, dirty and brown.
Here is the <u>grass</u>	It digs up the earth
So green and small.	And <u>makes a huge mound</u>.
Here <u>is</u> the <u>soil</u>	And here are the <u>bumps</u>
Such lovely colours, see.	<u>Full of dirt and clay</u>.
Here are the <u>badgers</u>	<u>Down in</u> the meadow
So wild and free.	Where we <u>like</u> to play.

Is the poem about good or bad changes now?

+ Tell them that they are now going to write their own poem about changes based on 'Walking round the town'.

How places change

 Group activities

Using the differentiated activity sheets

Activity sheet 1: This sheet is aimed at children who need a lot of support in writing a poem. They are required to complete two verses by cutting and pasting the correct words into the poem layout.

Activity sheet 2: This sheet is aimed at children who can use a word box to select words to complete a poem. They are also required to complete the last verse by themselves.

Activity sheet 3: This sheet is for more able children. They are required to write three verses of a poem without any support. They are also required to write about the poem they have written.

 Plenary session

Share the responses to the activity sheets. How many different words can fit the poems and still make sense? Did they find having a certain pattern to follow made it easier to write a poem? Do they think the changes made to the town (in the poem) were good or bad?

 Follow-up ideas for literacy

- ✦ Explore the use of questions further. Challenge the children to write some questions they would like to find the answers to. Perhaps they could be about their own local area. For example, 'How old is our school?' and 'What is the name of the street where the post office is?' You could make a class book of their questions and answers for everyone to share.
- ✦ Share other poems about how places/the environment change. (A good collection is *Earthways, Earthwise* selected by Judith Nicholls, OUP.)

- ✦ Ask the children to write about changes they have experienced, for example moving to a new house, re-decorating their bedroom, making a garden or having a new brother or sister. How did it affect them? What happened?
- ✦ Make a class non-fiction book entitled 'What we know about our town/village/city'. Ask people to come in and talk to the children about their local area. Take photographs and ask the children to write captions for them. Make lists of all the facilities in the area. Draw pictures of the types of houses found locally.

 Follow-up ideas for geography

- ✦ Go on a walk around the local area. Take photographs of things that are changing/ have recently changed. Make up a class book with captions and sentences about these changes. Mark the areas of change on a local map and display this with the book.
- ✦ Collect some magazine pictures that could be used to discuss before and after sequences. For example, a picture of a new supermarket and a picture of a derelict site. Ask the children to comment on whether they think the change has been for the better or the worse. Can they say why?

- ✦ Show the children a collection of pictures where improvements could be made, for example, a picture of a park with lots of litter in it, an old house that is falling down, an old factory, a polluted stream and so on. Share the pictures with the children and ask them to think of ways these areas might be changed so that they are improved. Are there any areas in their school or local region that could be changed for the better? How could they go about this?

Changes

Walking round the town

Walking round the town
What changes can we see?
A big new supermarket
Where a field used to be.

Walking round the town
What changes can we see?
An enormous green park
Where a dump used to be.

Walking round the town
What changes can we see?
A safe cycle path
Where a railway used to be.

Walking round the town
What changes can we see?
A big row of houses
Where an orchard used to be.

Where we used to play

Here are the trees
Standing big and tall.
Here is the hedge
So green and small.

Here are the flowers
Such lovely colours, see.
Here are the rabbits
So wild and free.

Here comes the bulldozer
Loud, dirty and brown.
It digs up the earth
And knocks the trees
down.

And here are the houses
All dull, dark and grey.
Gone is the meadow
Where we used to play.

Our Village

The people in our street
All met together
And decided that we could
Make our village better.

We picked up the litter
We planted lots of trees
We fixed the broken fences,
One, two, three.

And now our village is perfect
It's a lovely place to be,
Everything is clean and safe
Why don't you come and see?

◆ Changes ◆

◆Cut out the words and put them in the correct places so the poem makes sense.

Walking round the town

Walking round the [ ]

What changes can we see?

A bright fun [ ]

Where a factory used to be.

[ ]   round the town

What changes can we see?

A big row of [ ]

Where a field used to be.

town	playground
shops	Walking

©Hopscotch Educational Publishing

✦ Changes ✦

✦ Use words from the box to complete this poem so
   that it makes sense. Then write your own last verse.

Walking round the town
What changes can we see?
A large flat _____
Where some rubble used to be.

Walking round the _____
What changes can we see?
An exciting new _____
Where a _____ used to be.

Walking round the town
What _____ can we see?
A dangerous _____
Where some old _____ used to be.

Walking _____the town
What changes can we _____?
Some colourful new _____
Where an old sign _____ to be.

Walking round the town
What changes can we see?

_____

_____

changes
factory
used
carpark
paint
town
houses
sports centre
building site
see
round

Changes

◆ Write your own verses for the poem below by using the pattern of the first verse. Use a dictionary to help you.

Walking round the town
What changes can we see?
A brand new cinema
Where an old hall used to be.

Walking round the town
What changes can we see?

_____

_____

Walking round the town
What changes can we see?

_____

_____

_____

_____

_____

_____

◆ Now think about the changes that you have written about in this poem. Do you think they would be good or bad changes for the town?

©Hopscotch Educational Publishing

Chapter 5

Making places safe

 Literacy objectives

+ To identify simple questions and use text to find answers. To locate parts of text that give particular information including labelled diagrams and charts. (Y1: T3, T19)
+ To record answers to questions. (Y1: T2, T22)

 Geography objectives

(Unit 2)
+ To express views about making an area safer.
+ To recognise ways of changing the environment.

 Resources

+ Pictures of a street with lots of traffic, a street without any traffic, pedestrian crossings, a street with lots of cars parked and so on.

 Starting point: Whole class

+ Write the following question on the board: 'How can we make the area around our school safer?' Tell the children that they are going to be thinking about this question and will try to find out the answer by talking about it together, by looking at pictures and by looking at some information gathered by another school. Begin by asking them about their journey to school. What things have been done in their area to make it safer for children to walk to school? (For example, crossings, lollipop men or ladies, traffic calming measures and clearways outside the school.)
+ Show the children a picture of a street with lots of cars parked on it. Discuss why it might be dangerous to cross there. Explain that this is why schools have clearways/no parking areas.
+ Show them the picture of a street with lots of traffic on it. Compare this with the picture of a quiet street. Ask them where they would cross the busy road and why. Talk about what could be put in that street to make it safer. (Crossings and traffic calming measures.)
+ Ask the children to think about their own local area. Are there any places that are less safe than others? What changes could be made?

+ Tell them that they are now going to look at some information that another school gathered about ways of making the area around their school safer.

 Using the photocopiable text

+ Share an enlarged version of page 30 or provide each pair with a copy.
+ Write the following questions on the board:
  • What is the name of the school?
  • What did they want to find out?
  • How did they find this out?
  • How did they show their results?
  • What ideas did people come up with for making travelling to school safer?
  • Which of these ideas was the most popular?
  • Which idea was the second most popular?
  • Where do the people want a new crossing?
+ Go through each question to make sure the children understand them. Remind them that questions have a question mark at the end. Say that you want them to read page 30 to find the answers to all the above questions. Before reading the text, ask them where on the page they might find the answer to each question. Where should they look first? Why? Remind them that we often use abbreviations, especially on maps. In this case 'St' means both 'Saint' in the name of the school and 'Street'.
+ Go through each question together, agreeing where to look in the text and writing the answers on the board.
+ Challenge the children to think of their own questions to which they could find the answers using this text. For example: Which idea was the least popular? Where is the present crossing? On the corner of which streets is St Stephen's? How many people wanted new pavements built?
+ Discuss the ideas presented for St Stephen's School with reference to their own area. Would any of these ideas help improve the safety of their area? Can they think of more safety ideas?
+ Tell them that the children at St Stephen's School also tried to find out how to make their playground safer. Explain that they are now going to answer some questions about what the children at that school found out.

Making places safe

 ## Group activities

Using the differentiated activity sheets

Activity sheet 1: This sheet is aimed at children who need a lot of support in answering questions. The answers have been modelled for them on the page.

Activity sheet 2: This sheet is aimed at children who can use diagrams and graphs to locate information to answer questions.

Activity sheet 3: This sheet is for more able children. They are required to locate the parts of the text that will give them answers to a set of questions. They then record their answers.

 ## Plenary session

Share the responses to the activity sheets. Are they agreed on the answers? Where did they need to look for the answers to particular questions? Ask someone who completed Activity sheet 3 to read out their list of things to improve safety at their school. Discuss the changes that could take place and why.

 ## Follow-up ideas for literacy

- Ask the children to write their own questions prior to reading for information, perhaps relating to the class topic.
- Ask each child to write a different question (about anything) on a slip of paper. Then ask them to write a suitable answer to their question on another slip of paper. Put the papers into two separate bags. Ask individuals to pick out a paper from each bag to make funny questions and answers. They could be turned into a class poem.

- Ask the children to write about their own school area. Do they think anything is unsafe? What changes would they like to make it safer? They could write a letter to the headteacher expressing their concerns.
- Ask someone to come in and talk to the children about road safety. Have prepared some questions suggested by the children to ask the visitor. Make up a class book about road safety. Include the children's questions and answers.

 ## Follow-up ideas for geography

- Go on a walk around the local area. Take photographs of anything the children think could be improved to make it safer, such as a littered area, a busy road without a crossing or damaged street furniture. Back at school use the photographs to discuss ideas about how their local area can be improved. The children could do a survey like the St Stephen's School example where they ask people about their ideas for improving safety and write up or graph the results.

- Visit the local area to find out where pedestrian and lollipop crossings are located. Back at school mark these places on a local map. Discuss how close the crossings are to the school and whether or not the children think they are in the best places.
- Carry out a traffic count survey. Ask the children to count the number of cars that pass the school at different times of the day, for example 8.45am, 10am, 12 noon, 2pm and 3pm. (You could do the early time slot.) Graph the results. Discuss why there is a difference in traffic at different times and the safety implications of this.

Making our school area safer

What we wanted to find out
We wanted to find out how we could make it safer to travel to and from our school.

What we did
We asked the children, parents and teachers for their ideas. We wrote down what they said. Then we made some graphs and diagrams.

What we found out

Ideas for making it safer for children to travel to school

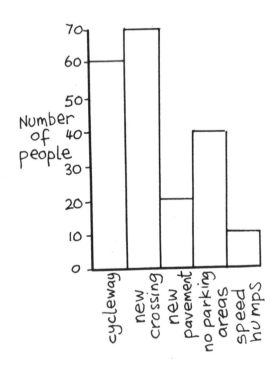

Map showing where new crossings are needed

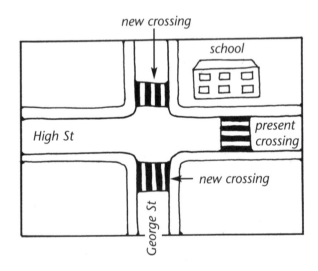

◆ Playground safety ◆

◆ The children at St Stephen's School took photographs of all the things that were not safe in their playground. Use them to complete the answers to the questions.

The swing has a broken seat.

The playground has holes in it.

The litter bin is broken.

There are lots of stones outside.

1.   What is wrong with the swing?
     The swing has a _____ seat.

2.   Why is the litter on the ground?
     The litter bin is _____.

3.   What is wrong with the playground?
     The ground has _____ in it.

4.   What else is wrong outside?
     There are lots of _____.

◆ Playground safety ◆

◆ Here are a graph and a diagram made by the children at St Stephen's School. Use them to complete the answers to the questions. Use the word box to help you.

Diagram showing unsafe things in the playground

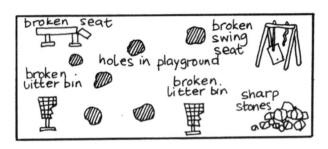

Ideas for making our playground safer

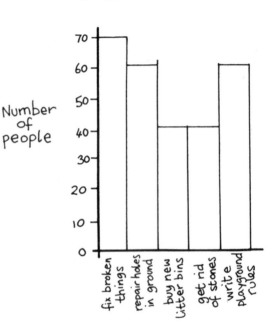

1. How many things were unsafe in the playground?

   There were 5 things that were unsafe: the swing, the ground, the seat, the stones and the _____.

2. How many people want to fix the broken things?_____

3. How many people want to write some playground rules?_____

4. What was wrong with the swing?

   The swing had a _____.

litter bins	70	60	broken seat

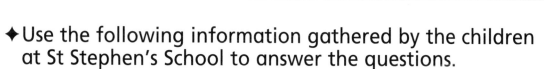
✦ Playground safety ✦

✦ Use the following information gathered by the children
   at St Stephen's School to answer the questions.

Making our playground safer

<u>What we wanted to find out</u>
We wanted to find out how we could make it safer in our school playground.

<u>What we did</u>
We took photographs of all the things that were unsafe in our playground. Then we asked
people how we could make it better. Then we made some graphs and diagrams.

<u>Diagram showing unsafe things
in the playground</u>

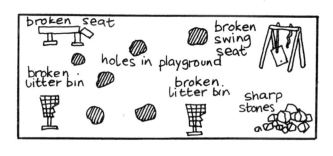

<u>Ideas for making our
playground safer</u>

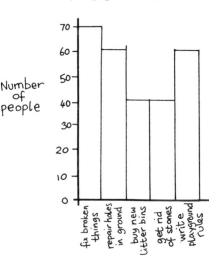

1.   What did the children at St. Stephen's take photographs of?

    _____

2.   What did most people want to do to make the playground safer?

    _____

3.   How many people want to write some playground rules?_____

4.   How many holes are there in the playground?_____

✦ On the back of this sheet, list some things you think could be
   done to make the playground safer at your own school.

Chapter 6

The seaside – 1

 Literacy objectives

✦ To collect words linked to a particular topic. (Y2: T1, W10)
✦ To use simple poetry structures, substitute own ideas and write new lines. (Y2: T1, T12)

 Geography objectives

(Unit 4)
✦ To identify the main features of the seaside.
✦ To relate specific human and physical features to a given place.

 Resources

✦ Pictures of the seaside showing human and physical features, such as cliffs, caves, sand, piers, buoys and lighthouses.
✦ Map/atlas showing closest seaside towns to own area.

 Starting point: Whole class

✦ Ask the children if they have ever been to the seaside. Talk about why people like to go there. What sorts of things do they usually do there? Discuss how people often go to the seaside on holidays or weekends to get fresh air, exercise and relaxation. (If your school is in a seaside area, you can still ask the children these questions.)
✦ Show the children a map/atlas indicating the closest seaside towns to where they live. Have they ever visited these places? What did they do and see there? (If your school is in a seaside area, you could ask the children about other seaside places they have visited.)
✦ Use the collection of pictures to discuss the human and physical features usually found at the seaside. Ask the children to identify the features they can see. List them on the board. Can they think of any other features they have seen at the seaside that are not shown in the pictures? Add these to the list.
✦ Tell the children that they are now going to share a poem about the seaside. Explain that you would like them to look out for any of the words on the list as you read it.

 Using the photocopiable text

✦ Share an enlarged version of page 36 or provide each pair with a copy.
✦ Share the poem. What words did they find that were on the class list? Underline them. Add any new words from the poem that were not on the list.
✦ Explain that the poem is an action poem. What kinds of actions could they make up for each line? Agree the actions. Perform each line together to make sure that they can say the words and do the actions. Then perform the whole poem together.
✦ Tell the children that we could include other words from the list of seaside features to make a new poem. Give them an example of how we could substitute words to make a new poem. For example:

> Here are the sand dunes.
> Here is the sand.
> Here are the rock pools
> where the crabs stand.
> Here are the boats
> that bob and rock.
> And here is the pier
> where the boats dock.

✦ Make up actions for the new poem. Perform it together.
✦ Tell the children that they will now have the opportunity to use their own ideas to replace some words/lines in the poem to create another version.

The seaside – 1

 Group activities

Using the differentiated activity sheets

Activity sheet 1: This sheet is aimed at children who need a lot of support in using a simple poetry structure to write new lines. They are provided with a limited choice of words.

Activity sheet 2: This sheet is aimed at children who can use their own ideas to complete a given poem.

Activity sheet 3: This sheet is for more able children who can use the structure of the given poem to create their own.

 Plenary session

Share the responses to the activity sheets. How many sea words did they think of? Can any new words be added to the class list? How many different versions of the poem were created? Which one do they like best? Why? How could their poems be improved? Did they enjoy having a set structure to follow when writing the poem? Challenge the children to write some more poems using the same structure but different topics.

 Follow-up ideas for literacy

- Make a class dictionary of seaside words. Ask the children to write definitions for the words. Encourage them to use the dictionary to write their own sentences/stories/factual information about the seaside.
- Share stories about the seaside and relate these to the children's own experiences. Discuss whether the story events have happened to them. What would they do in the same circumstances?
- Ask the children to collect seaside poems to make a class anthology. They could write a sentence saying why they like the poem they have chosen.

- If possible, arrange a visit to the seaside. Ask the children to list and draw the things they see. Help them to write a report about the visit linked to the language of time, for example: 'First we …'; 'Then we …'; 'After that we …'; 'Finally we …'
- Ask the children to write some simple instructions to do with the seaside, for example 'How to make a sandcastle'. They could draw and label diagrams to go with the instructions.

 Follow-up ideas for geography

- Ask the children to consider how the seaside is different from their own local area. (If your school is in a seaside area you could compare two different seaside places or your locality with an inland locality.) They could cut out magazine pictures to show the typical human and physical features of each place.
- Invite a grandparent to talk to the children about what the seaside was like in the past. Encourage them to make comparisons with the seaside today. Make a chart showing things that are the same and things that are different. Challenge the children to write about what they have learned.

- Ask the children to bring in postcards from seaside holidays. Add travel brochures to the collection. Ask the children to use the information to name five different seaside holiday places in the world. Provide them with atlases. Can they find these places? Ask them to use the pictures to make a holiday poster about one of the places. Encourage them to list the geographical features of the location.

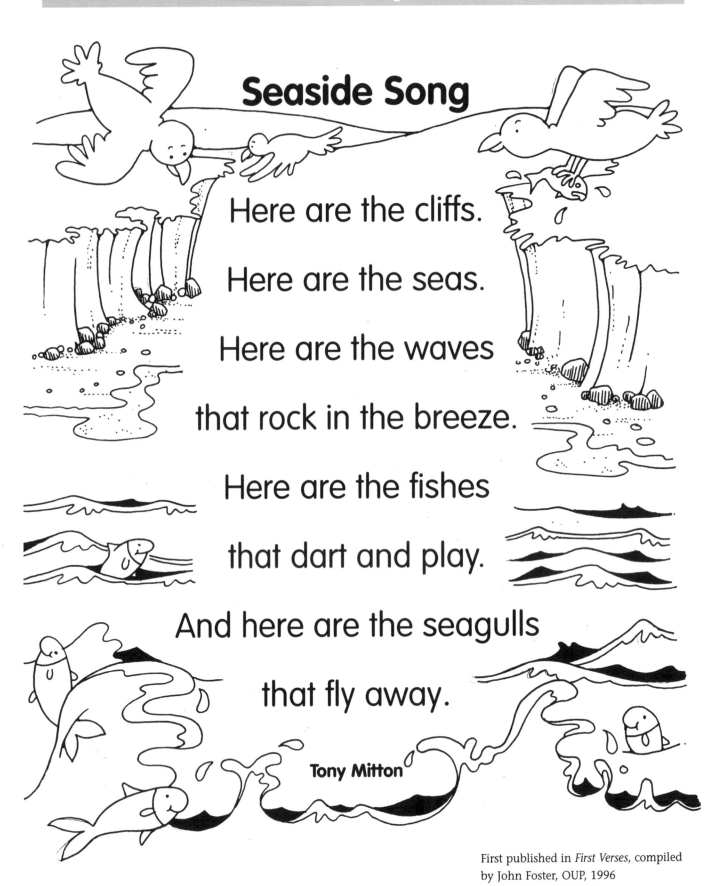

Seaside Song

Here are the cliffs.

Here are the seas.

Here are the waves

that rock in the breeze.

Here are the fishes

that dart and play.

And here are the seagulls

that fly away.

Tony Mitton

First published in *First Verses*, compiled by John Foster, OUP, 1996

◆ S e a s i d e   p o e m ◆

✦Label the seaside picture. Use words from the box.

| waves |
| cliffs |
| seaweed |
| pebbles |

✦Now use the same words from above to complete this poem.

The seaside

Here is the _____

Here is the shore.

Here are the _____

Listen to them roar.

Here are the _____
both large and small

And here are the _____
standing big and tall.

✦ S e a s i d e p o e m ✦

✦You are going to write your own version of the poem
  below. Choose from the words in the box or use words
  of your own. Use a dictionary to help you.

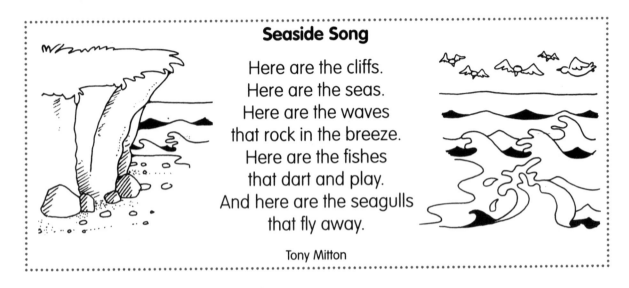

Seaside Song

Here are the cliffs.
Here are the seas.
Here are the waves
that rock in the breeze.
Here are the fishes
that dart and play.
And here are the seagulls
that fly away.

Tony Mitton

The seaside

Here are the _____

Here is the _____

Here are the _____

    Listen to them roar.

Here are the _____

that _____

And here are the _____

_____

sand
pebbles
waves
seaweed
cliffs
pier
rocks
shore
beach
caves
buoy
lighthouse
ship
dune

✦ Seaside poem ✦

✦You are going to write your own version of the poem below. Write a list of words you could use in the box. Then use the words to complete your poem. Use a dictionary to help you.

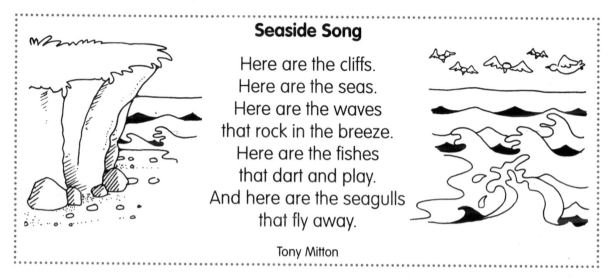

Seaside Song

Here are the cliffs.
Here are the seas.
Here are the waves
that rock in the breeze.
Here are the fishes
that dart and play.
And here are the seagulls
that fly away.

Tony Mitton

✦Write your poem here.

Here _____

Here _____

Here _____

that _____

Here _____

that _____

And here _____

that _____

My word list
pebbles
sand

The seaside – 2

 Literacy objectives

✦ To discuss familiar story themes and link them to own experiences. (Y2: T1, T6)
✦ To use story structure to write about own experiences. (Y1: T1, T10)

 Geography objectives

(Unit 4)
✦ To compare own locality with a different locality.
✦ To compare lifestyle at home with living by the sea.

 Resources

✦ Pictures/photographs of typical human and physical features of the seaside (beach, cliffs, beach huts, pier) and of the children's local area (house types, typical shops/streets/parks).

 Starting point: Whole class

✦ Tell the children that they are going to compare where they live with living by the sea. (If your school is at the seaside, you can make comparisons with another seaside place or another locality that is different in some way.) What do the children think it might be like to live at this seaside place? How might it be different from living where they live now? Use the photographs/ pictures to make comparisons. Draw up a chart, such as the one below, to make a summary of the discussion.

 Using the photocopiable text

✦ Tell the children that they are now going to share a story about some children who live in a seaside town. Ask them to try and imagine what the town might be like as you read the story.
✦ Share the story on page 42. (Enlarge it on a photocopier or make enough copies for each pair.)
✦ Discuss the story setting. What was Torrington-on-Sea like? Did it have any features already listed in the class chart? Can any new features be added to the chart? What kinds of things did Nat and Sarra enjoy doing in Torrington? How does this compare with where the children in the class live? Would they like to be able to do these things? Or do they prefer living where they are now? Why?
✦ Talk about what happened to Sarra in the story. Have they ever been lost? How did it feel? Have they ever lost someone or something? Did they panic like Nat did? Where would it be easy for a young child in their town to get lost – the shopping centre perhaps? How would they go about finding them? Where would they think to look first?
✦ Tell the children that they are going to write their own story now about where they live. Ask them to think of something that has happened to them in their town – perhaps they also got lost one day or the town had a special event, such as a fair or a parade. What happened to them when they were there? They could spend a few minutes talking with a partner to help them develop an idea for their story.
✦ Explain the story planners to the children. Remind them that they could use the words in the chart of things in their town to help them.

	seaside town	our town
where people live	bungalows caravans hotels houses	terraced houses high-rise flats semi-detached houses
things to see	beach sea cliffs rock pools sand dunes	parks buildings
things to do and visit	swim play on beach amusement arcade coastal walk shops sea life centre	sports centre cinema shops playground park museum
shops/ buildings	lighthouse beach huts tea shops	supermarket shopping centre offices

Literacy through geography
KS1: Y1–2

The seaside – 2

 ## Group activities

Using the differentiated activity sheets

Activity sheet 1: This sheet is aimed at children who need a lot of support in writing a story. They have the option of simply drawing what happens in their story.

Activity sheet 2: This sheet is aimed at children who need the support of a writing frame to organise their story.

Activity sheet 3: This sheet is for more able children who are able to use given guidelines to develop their story.

 ## Plenary session

Share the children's stories. Did using a story planner help them to structure their story? What kinds of experiences did the children write about? Were they happy ones? Sad? Scary? Funny? Why did they decide to write about the experience they chose? Could this experience happen in any town or was it peculiar to where they live? Why?

 ## Follow-up ideas for literacy

- Ask the children to write another story about Nat and Sarra. They could build up an image of what Torrington-on-Sea is like by drawing or cutting out pictures. They could then imagine other adventures the children could have in the town. Make the stories into individual books and display them with the pictures of Torrington.
- Use the discussion about places to develop the use of capital letters further. Where are capitals used? (Place names, streets, rivers, people's names, shop names and so on.)

- Explore the use of commas in the 'Lost!' story. Explain how commas are used in lists. Ask the children to make up lists, using commas, of the types of shops and places to visit in their town or the names of streets where they live and so on. For example, 'In my street there is a shop, a school, a bus stop, some houses and a park.' The children could then go on to draw and label the items in the list to make a geographical profile of where they live.

 ## Follow-up ideas for geography

- Ask the children to use a key to label the human and physical features of a seaside area and their own area on a drawing done from photographs.
- The children could make up a map of what they think Torrington-on-Sea might be like. Use the story for clues. They could invent street names and other human and physical features and mark these on the map. This could develop into the children creating a more accurate map of their own local area.

- Use an atlas to find the names of seaside places throughout the UK. The children could write to tourist information centres to obtain information about some of these places. How similar to and different from each other are they? Do all these seaside places have certain things in common? Make a list. How does this list compare with the chart of the children's ideas developed at the beginning of the lesson on 'Lost!'?

Lost!

Nat and Sarra lived in Torrington-on-Sea. Their house was a small bungalow in Seaside Close. It had a wonderful view of the sea and the Torrington lighthouse at the end of the point. In their garden was an old rowing boat that one of the fishermen had given them. They spent many hours playing in it pretending to be great sea explorers.

Nat and Sarra also loved to play on the sea front. There they could run in and out of all the buildings that lined the street. There was an icecream shop, a gift shop, a restaurant, a post office, three tea shops, a fish and chip shop and, best of all, a long pier with an amusement arcade at the end. It was on the pier that Sarra went missing! They had been walking along the pier to the arcade. Nat had been kicking a can along when it suddenly disappeared down a deep hole. He lay down on the wooden floor to peer into the hole but he couldn't find it. When he stood up again, Sarra had gone!

He was frantic with worry. His mother had always told him to take care of his little sister and now she had gone - simply vanished. He ran along to the arcade, calling her name. He looked everywhere but there was no sign of her.

Nat raced back to the beach. He searched around the beach huts and the lifeboat house but she was nowhere to be seen. He ran all the way to the small cave at the foot of the cliffs where she loved to play at low tide but still he couldn't find her. "Mum will kill me!" he thought and he began to panic.

He wandered slowly back to the pier trying to work out what he was going to say to his mum, when he heard her laughing. He knew her funny little giggle anywhere! And there she was, sitting with the others watching Punch and Judy! She hadn't even realised he had been looking for her. She had wandered off to watch the show when Nat had first lost his can and in his panic, Nat had raced straight past her twice! Nat felt so silly he didn't even give her a telling off!

Activity 1

Name _____

 A story about where I live

◆ You are going to write a story about where you live. Complete the following story plan.

A picture of my house	A picture of my town

◆ Now draw and write about something that happened to you.

One day

✦ A story about where I live ✦

✦You are going to write a story about where you live. Complete the following story plan. Use words in the box to help you. Continue on the back of the sheet.

I live in _____(town) in a street called

_____. My house is _____

_____. From my house I can

see_____.

My town is very _____. It has a _____,

a_____ and a _____.

I like to play in _____.

<u>One day</u>_____

_____

_____

_____

_____

_____

| small | large | shops | park | roads | garden |
| nice | post office | sports centre | cinema | | |

✦ A story about where I live ✦

✦ Complete the following plan for a story about where you live. Use a dictionary to help you.

Write about where you live. Describe your house and street. What do they look like? What can you see from your house?

Write about the village, town or city where you live. What kinds of shops and entertainment places does it have? Where do you like to go? Where do you play?

Now write about something that happened to you where you live. Who was with you? How did you feel? What happened in the end?

Continue on the back of this sheet.

Places – 1

 Literacy objectives

- ✦ To collect words linked to a particular topic. (Y2: T2, W10)
- ✦ To use dictionaries to locate words. (Y2: T2, T16)
- ✦ To understand that dictionaries and glossaries give definitions. (Y2: T2, T17)
- ✦ To make a simple glossary linked to a topic. (Y2: T2, T20)

 Geography objectives

(Unit 3)
- ✦ To identify the physical and human features of a place.
- ✦ To understand how an island is different from the mainland.

 Resources

- ✦ *Katie Morag and the Two Grandmothers* by Mairi Hedderwick, Red Fox.
- ✦ An atlas that shows the location of Scotland and the Western Isles.
- ✦ Pictures and photographs of an island in the Inner Hebrides.
- ✦ Dictionaries. Books that contain a glossary.

 Starting point: Whole class

- ✦ Share the story of *Katie Morag and the Two Grandmothers*. Discuss what happens in the story. Explain the differences between an island and the mainland in order to help the children understand the characters' names, 'Grannie Island' and 'Grannie Mainland'.
- ✦ Talk about the story's setting, using an atlas to show the location of Scotland and the Western Isles. Use the pictures in the storybook and the photographs/pictures of an island in the Inner Hebrides to talk about the physical and human landscapes of the island of Struay.
- ✦ Ask the children to identify suitable words to go into two columns, one headed 'physical' and the other 'human'. For example:

physical	human
island	farm
coast	bridge
bay	road
stream	jetty
loch	well
hills	village

- ✦ Ask the children to tell you how they could find out what the words in the two columns mean, especially words such as 'loch', 'bay' and 'jetty'.
- ✦ Revise how to find words in a dictionary by looking up the meaning of some of the words. Share the definitions.
- ✦ Explain that information books often have a glossary at the back to explain the meaning of words in the book. Show them some examples from books.

 Using the photocopiable text

- ✦ Explain to the children that you are going to show them how to make a glossary by using an example from a book about America.
- ✦ Share page 48. (Enlarge it on a photocopier or make enough copies for each pair.)
- ✦ What do the children notice about the way the glossary is set out? Talk about how the words are listed alphabetically. Ask questions to elicit their understanding, for example 'What is the definition of "forest"?', 'What word is first in the glossary?' and 'What word comes after "river"?'
- ✦ Write three or four words from the two columns on the board, for example 'loch', 'farm', 'bay' and 'well'. List them by agreeing their alphabetical order. Ask the children to use dictionaries to look up the definitions of the words. Write them next to the words.
- ✦ Tell the children that they will now be doing an activity where they make up their own glossary about the island of Struay.

Places – 1

 ## Group activities

Using the differentiated activity sheets

Activity sheet 1: This sheet is aimed at children who need a lot of support. They are required to match words to their definitions and complete a given glossary using these words.

Activity sheet 2: This sheet is aimed at children who are able to use a dictionary to find definitions and can order words alphabetically.

Activity sheet 3: This sheet is for more able children. They are required to write the definitions of eight words and then order them alphabetically.

 ## Plenary session

Share the responses to the activity sheets. Are they all agreed on the order of the words in the glossary? What things did they need to remember when looking up definitions? When ordering the words? How useful do they think a glossary of words to go with the Katie Morag book would be? How would it help the readers? When do they think they might use a glossary?

 ## Follow-up ideas for literacy

- Make a class book about the children's own local area. Agree a glossary to include in the book. Make sure the list includes both physical and human terms.
- Ask the children to find information about other islands. They could make a tourist guide or design postcards to advertise the island.
- Have fun by asking the children to write a set of instructions on how to make a dirty sheep clean! Remind them to use the words and picture clues in the storybook to help them.

- Ask the children to imagine going on a visit to Struay. What would they see? Who might they meet? What things might they do? Make a large collage of the island and put the children's writing around it.
- Explore family trees. Ask the children to work out a family tree for the family in the story. They could then write out their own family tree or make up an ideal one!

 ## Follow-up ideas for geography

- Draw a map of the island of Struay and ask the children to draw and label places mentioned in the story.
- Draw a map of the children's own local area. Ask them to draw and label places they know. Compare this map with the one of Struay. Make a list of the differences between the two places.
- Compare the types of transport used on Struay with those of the children's own local area. Why do they think cars are not used on Struay? Which type of

transport do they think would be the most useful to islanders? Why?
- Ask the children to invent an island of their own! Ask them to draw a map/diagram and label the main human and physical features on their island. Encourage the more able to find out about other physical landscape features not explored in the storybook, such as spits, cliffs, arches, gullies and valleys, and to use these in their diagrams.

Glossary

desert	a place that has very few plants and little rain
farm	a place where humans grow crops or breed animals
forest	a large area of trees
house	a building used as a home
lake	an area of water surrounded by land
meadow	an area of grassland
mine	a place where minerals or stones are dug up out of the ground
mountain	an area of land higher than a hill
railway	a track for trains to run on
river	a large stream
road	a path or way on which people travel from one place to another
sawmill	a factory where trees are sawn into planks of wood
stream	a small river

◆ Glossary ◆

◆Match these words with their correct meanings.
One has been done for you.

hill   land with water all around it

mainland   the name for a lake in Scotland

bay   an area of higher ground

island   the main area of land

loch   an inward bend of the shore

◆Now complete the glossary below using
the words above.

bay   an inward bend of the _____

hill   an area of higher _____

island   land with _____ all around it

_____   the name for a lake in Scotland

mainland   the main area of _____

✦ Glossary ✦

✦Match these words with their correct meanings. Write a
definition for the word left over. Use a dictionary to help you.

hill   _____

mainland   the name for a lake in Scotland

bay   a landing area for boats

island   the main area of land

loch   an inward bend of the shore

jetty   an area of higher ground

✦Now rewrite the words and definitions as a glossary.
The first and last ones have been done for you.

bay   an inward bend of the shore

_____   _____

_____   _____

_____   _____

_____   _____

mainland   the main area of land

✦ Glossary ✦

✦ Use a dictionary to write the definitions of
these words.

jetty _____

mainland _____

island _____

bay _____

hill _____

loch _____

stream _____

sea _____

✦ Now rewrite the words in alphabetical order as
they would appear in a glossary.

1 _____   5 _____

2 _____   6 _____

3 _____   7 _____

4 _____   8 _____

Chapter 9

Places – 2

 Literacy objectives

+ To collect antonyms and discuss differences in meaning. (Y2: T2, W11)

 Geography objectives

(Unit 3)
+ To recognise and understand similar and different features of two contrasting places.

 Resources

+ *Katie Morag and the Two Grandmothers* by Mairi Hedderwick, Red Fox.

 Starting point: Whole class

+ The story of *Katie Morag and the Two Grandmothers* should already have been shared with the children before this lesson.
+ Ask the children to remind you of the story of Katie Morag. Where did she live? What was the island like? Share the two page illustration of the island at the front of the book to talk about the physical and human features in more detail. Discuss the physical features, such as mountains, hills, seashore, bays and streams, and the human features, such as the buildings, road, jetty, farm and bridge.
+ Ask the children to tell you how they think the island might compare with a city. What things (physical and human) might be the same? What things might be different? Make two lists on the board.
+ Tell the children that they are now going to look at a picture of a city to compare with the island.

 Using the photocopiable text

+ Share page 54. (Enlarge it on a photocopier or make enough copies for each pair.) Read out loud the labels and talk about what can be seen in the picture.
+ Look at the illustration from the book and page 54 side by side. What do the children notice that is different about the two places? What is the same? How many of their earlier suggestions about the differences and similarities between the island and the city were correct?

+ Tell the children you now want them to think of words to describe how different the two places are. Explain that we could use words that are opposite in meaning and that these words are called 'antonyms'. Give them several examples, such as 'big' and 'small', 'light' and 'heavy', and 'old' and 'young'.
+ Draw a column on the board for the island with appropriate subheadings and write in some words, for example:

The island
streets
> clean
> narrow
> few
> safe
> uncrowded
> calm
> quiet

+ Can the children think of words for the city streets that are opposite in meaning to these? (Dirty, wide, many, smooth, dangerous, crowded, busy, noisy.) Write these in a column headed 'The city'. Discuss the differences in meaning of the words.
+ Continue adding antonyms to the columns, for example:

The island	**The city**
houses	houses
low	tall
old	new
tidy	untidy
light	dark
far (apart)	close
small	big
landscape	landscape
hilly	flat

+ Tell the children they will now be doing some more work using antonyms.

Places – 2

 ## Group activities

Using the differentiated activity sheets

Activity sheet 1: This sheet is aimed at children who need a lot of support. They are required to match words that are opposite in meaning.

Activity sheet 2: This sheet is aimed at children who are able to write their own antonyms for a given list of words.

Activity sheet 3: This sheet is for more able children. They are required to construct their own lists of antonyms to describe the differences between the two pictures.

 ## Plenary session

Share the responses to the activity sheets. Are they all agreed on the words that are opposites? Can some words have several different meanings and therefore different antonyms? (for example 'light' – 'heavy', 'dark'). Explore how using a prefix such as 'un' can make antonyms. Challenge the children to make words into antonyms using this prefix, such as 'happy', 'healthy', 'safe' and 'usual'.

 ## Follow-up ideas for literacy

+ Use the cityscape picture to discuss story settings. Build up a story about the scene together and then ask the children to write or complete the story in their own words.
+ The children could make a glossary to go with the cityscape picture. Encourage them to find out the meaning of one or two terms each and then produce a class or group glossary.
+ Share some poems about the city and the country. Use the poems to continue discussions about the similarities and differences between places.

+ Ask the children to imagine that they are Katie Morag and that they have gone on a trip from the island to the city in the picture. How do they think Katie might feel? What things do they think she would enjoy/dislike? Why? What might happen to her on her visit? The children could write a story about her adventure or they could write a letter back home to Struay telling her family about her visit.

 ## Follow-up ideas for geography

+ Ask the children to draw and label a picture of the area where they live. How does this compare with the island of Struay and the city in the picture on page 54?
+ Talk to the children about their likes and dislikes about where they live. What things are good about their area? What things are poor? What do they think might be the good and bad things about living on the island of Struay and in the city in the picture? How can people make their area a better place to be? The children could design a poster telling others how to improve their own local area.

+ Ask the children to find information about the Western Isles of Scotland. They could make a collage map of the area that contains pictures and information about the region.
+ Ask the children to find pictures of places in magazines that are different from each other, for example a desert and a rainforest or a flat plain and a mountainous area. Make a display of the contrasting places. The children could write some sentences about what is the same and what is different about the places.

A cityscape

pub

traffic lights

flats

pavement

alleyway

shop

park

✦ Opposites ✦

✦Look at the two pictures below.

✦The words below describe things in the two pictures.
Match the words that are opposite in meaning.
One has been done for you.

tall	many
small	noisy
few	big
old	pointed
quiet	short
round	new

✦ Opposites ✦

✦ Look at the two pictures below.

✦ Write the words that are opposite in meaning to those below to describe the two pictures. The first one has been done for you.

pointed	_round_	wide	_____
old	_____	small	_____
tall	_____	near	_____
few	_____	clean	_____
quiet	_____	smooth	_____
steep	_____	untidy	_____
busy	_____	light	_____

◆ Opposites ◆

◆Look at the two pictures below. Think of words that could be used to describe the things in the pictures.

◆Now complete the lists below by writing words and their opposites to describe the pictures. One has been done for you.

pointed	round	_____	_____
_____	_____	_____	_____
_____	_____	_____	_____
_____	_____	_____	_____
_____	_____	_____	_____
_____	_____	_____	_____
_____	_____	_____	_____

Places – 3

 Literacy objectives

+ To scan a text to find specific sections, for example key words or phrases or subheadings. (Y2: T3, T16)
+ To make simple notes from non-fiction texts to use in own writing. (Y2: T3, T19)

 Geography objectives

(Unit 5)

+ To learn about the location of other places.
+ To learn about the types of transport used to get to other places.
+ To develop a sense of distance associated with travel.

 Resources

+ Pictures of different types of transport, such as a car, bus, boat, bicycle, train and plane (include a monorail if possible).
+ Postcards of different places – one quite close to where the children live, one a little further away and others in more distant places in the UK and overseas.
+ Atlases.

 Starting point: Whole class

+ Tell the children that they are going to learn how people travel to different places. Show them the pictures of the different types of transport. Which ones have the children travelled in themselves? Display the pictures where the children can see them.
+ Show them the postcard of a place very near to where they live. Discuss where it is. Agree how close it is using a simple scale such as 'very near', 'near', 'far away' and 'very far away'. Which of the types of transport could they use to get there? How long do they think it might take them to get there? Which transport couldn't they use? Why?
+ Repeat the above with the other postcards, using an atlas to locate the places in relation to where the children live.
+ Tell the children they are now going to look at the writing on a postcard from Australia to see what information they can find about how the people have travelled on their holiday.

 Using the photocopiable text

+ Show the children an enlarged version of page 60 but do not read it yet. Explain that it is a postcard from Peta, who is on holiday in Australia, to her friend Maddy. Have any of the children or their relatives/friends been to Australia? How far away is it? How could we travel to get there?
+ Explain that they are going to make some notes about Peta's holiday. Tell them that you want them to make a list of how Peta travelled each day. Where might they look to find out what Peta did on Tuesday? Ask someone to come and point to where they might look. Where might they look to find out what she did on Friday? Explain that sometimes we do not need to read a whole piece of text in order to find information. Tell them how looking for subheadings, such as the days of the week on the postcard, can help them to know where to look on the page.
+ Write the word 'car' on the board. Challenge the children to scan the text to find the word – again without reading the whole text first. On what day did they travel in a car? Repeat this for other transport words such as 'train' and 'plane'.
+ Make a summary of each day of the journey (including Monday) and the type of transport used. That is:

> Monday – plane
> Tuesday – ferry, train
> Wednesday – monorail
> Thursday – car
> Friday – bus

+ Then share the whole text together. Where did PETA travel to? Ask the children to name the places, such as Darling Harbour and Bondi Beach. Do they think the Blue Mountains might be very close to the city of Sydney or further away? Why do they think this?
+ Tell the children they will now be doing some more work finding out about how people travel to places.

Places – 3

 ## Group activities

Using the differentiated activity sheets

Activity sheet 1: This sheet is aimed at children who need a lot of support. They are required to find key words and to complete sentences using these words.

Activity sheet 2: This sheet is aimed at children who are able to scan a text to find words and then use given information to complete sentences.

Activity sheet 3: This sheet is for more able children. They are required to make a list of the places visited and the transport used and then use this information to write their own sentences.

 ## Plenary session

Share the responses to the activity sheets. Use an atlas to find the places mentioned in the postcard, showing them how to use the index to find the correct page. Discuss how near or far the postcard places are to where the children live. As a follow-up, ask the children to write their own postcards to each other about the places they have visited and how they travelled there.

 ## Follow-up ideas for literacy

- Using the collection of postcards, challenge the children to think up some questions they would like to ask about these places. Provide them with information books about the places. Show them how to use the contents and index pages to help them find the answers.
- Write to a school in a place far away from the children's own area. Arrange for a class to write postcards to your class and vice versa.
- Ask the children to find more information about different forms of transport. They could make

up individual books about a different type of transport each to put in the school or class library.
- Share poems about travel and/or transport. Robert Louis Stevenson's *A Child's Garden of Verses* has a good selection, such as 'From a railway carriage' and 'Travel'.
- Ask the children to write an imaginative story about a journey to another place. They could invent a place or find out about a real place. The stories could be presented in transport-shaped books, that is, in the shape of a boat, a plane or a train.

 ## Follow-up ideas for geography

- Ask people to come in and talk to the children about different places they have visited – in the UK and abroad. Ask the children to prepare some questions about what the weather is like there and what things there are to see and do. Ask the visitor to bring postcards, photographs and artefacts from the place. Make some passports for the children and at the end of each visit, stamp them with the name of the place. Ask the children to prepare a suitcase of suitable holiday clothes for each place by cutting out pictures from magazines.

- 'Visit' a different place in the UK and abroad each day (or week) by marking the place on a wall map, discussing how we could travel there and speculating what the place might be like.
- Set up a travel agency in the classroom. Put lots of brochures on display. Encourage the children to select a holiday destination and use the brochures and other information books to find out as much as they can about the place. Ask them to consider the similarities and differences between these places and their own local area.

A postcard from Australia

Dear Maddy

We arrived here on Monday. It's great! But the plane trip was really horrible. Here's what we've been doing:

<u>Tuesday</u>

Went on the ferry across the harbour to the zoo. Caught the train back to our hotel. It went across the Sydney Harbour bridge! What a fantastic sight!

<u>Wednesday</u>

Went on the monorail to Darling Harbour.

<u>Thursday</u>

We hired a car and went to the Blue Mountains.

<u>Friday</u>

We caught a bus to Bondi Beach for the day.

  I'll write again soon,
    Love Peta

Maddy Elvin
12 Forest Rd
Corsham
Wiltshire
UK

◆ A postcard from England ◆

◆Find the following words on the postcard below and circle them.

car   train   boat   cycle

Dear Peta
Glad you are enjoying Sydney. We have been visiting a few places too in the holidays. This is where we went:
Bradford-on-Avon
We took the train from Bath. It is a really old town.
Castle Combe
Dad drove us there in his new car last week. We had a picnic.
Bathampton
We went on a boat up to Bathampton. It was really good! Then we went on a cycle ride back to Bath.

Please write soon,

Love Maddy

Peta White
Harbour Hotel
Sydney
Australia

◆How many places did Maddy visit?   1   2   3   4

◆Complete the following. Choose words from the box.

Maddy went to Bradford-on-Avon by _____.

Maddy went to Bathampton on a _____.

Maddy went to Castle Combe by _____.

Maddy went on a _____ ride back to Bath.

| cycle |
| car |
| train |
| boat |

◆ A postcard from England ◆

◆Look at the postcard below. Circle all the different types of transport used by Maddy and her family.

Dear Peta
Glad you are enjoying Sydney. We have been visiting a few places too in the holidays. This is where we went:
<u>Bradford-on-Avon</u>
We took the train from Bath. It is a really old town.
<u>Castle Combe</u>
Dad drove us there in his new car last week. We had a picnic.
<u>Bathampton</u>
We went on a boat up to Bathampton. It was really good! Then we went on a cycle ride back to Bath.

Please write soon,

     Love Maddy

Peta White
Harbour Hotel
Sydney
Australia

◆Complete the sentences below to show how Maddy travelled to each place she visited.

Maddy and her family went to _____

by train. They travelled there from _____.

Maddy's _____ drove her to _____

in his new _____. Maddy went on a _____

to _____. Then they _____ back to

_____.

◆ A postcard from England ◆

◆ Look at the postcard below. Circle all the different types of transport used by Maddy and her family.

Dear Peta

Glad you are enjoying Sydney. We have been visiting a few places too in the holidays. This is where we went:

Bradford-on-Avon

We took the train from Bath. It is a really old town.

Castle Combe

Dad drove us there in his new car last week. We had a picnic.

Bathampton

We went on a boat up to Bathampton. It was really good! Then we went on a cycle ride back to Bath.

Please write soon,

Love Maddy

Peta White
Harbour Hotel
Sydney
Australia

◆ List all the places Maddy visited and how she got there.

◆ On the back of this sheet, use your list to write four sentences about where Maddy went on her holiday and how she travelled to each place.